Hello Kitty's Fall Surprise

by Kris Hirschmann
Illustrated by Sachiho Hino

SCHOLASTIC INC.

ISBN 978-0-545-49855-5

© 1976, 2012 SANRIO CO., LTD. Used Under License.

All rights reserved. Published by Scholastic Inc., 557 Broadway, New York, NY

10012. Scholastic and assorted logos are trademarks and/or registered trademarks of Scholastic Inc.

12 11 10 9 8 7 6 5 4 3 2   13 14 15 16 17/0

Printed in the U.S.A.   40

This edition first printing, September 2012

, , and  were playing

near the  one fall day.

The  was shining.

The  had hiked all morning.

Now they wanted something

new to do.

They decided to collect  and

.

All of the 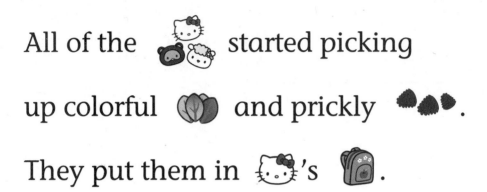 started picking

up colorful and prickly .

They put them in 's .

 spotted several pretty

lying together. She picked

up the .

Under the  was a big

pile of 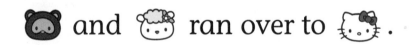.

 was excited to find them.

 and ran over to .

They admired the .

 suggested taking them  .

They could 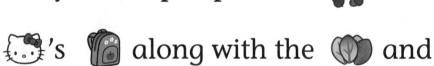 and them

together and each make their own

fall .

Everyone agreed that was a fun idea!

Everyone helped put the into

's along with the and

.

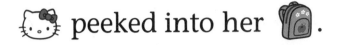 peeked into her .

There were many . But it will be

fun to have even more!

The started to search. They

found several more piles of .

They picked up the piles and put

them into 's .

Just then 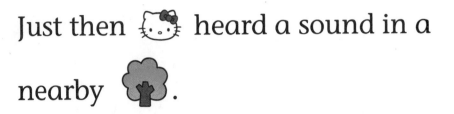 heard a sound in a

nearby .

She looked up and saw a

sitting on a .

The looked at with its

round brown . It wiggled

its furry .

The looked very sad.

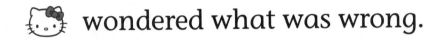 wondered what was wrong.

The 🐿️ looked at the spot

where had found the

first pile of 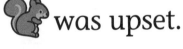 .

Then it looked at 🐱 and wiggled

its 🐿️ again.

Suddenly, 🐱 knew why the

🐿️ was upset.

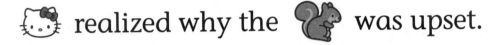 realized why the was upset.

They had just collected all of its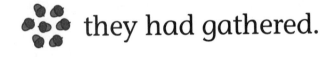

for the winter!

They knew they had to give back the

they had gathered.

They decided to find some more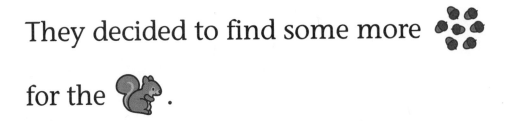

for the 🐿️ .

🐑 saw some  under a 🌳 .

🐻 found a whole bunch next

to a 🪵 .

🐱 spotted even more behind a ⬭ .

The 🐻🐱🐑 piled all the 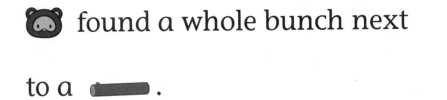 they

found at the base of a 🌳 .

Then they walked away, turned, and

watched the 🐿️ .

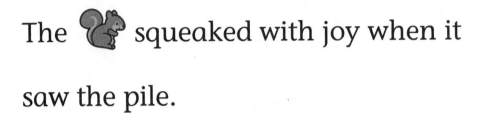

The 🐿 squeaked with joy when it saw the pile.

It ran down the 🌳 and picked up two 🌰. It carried the 🌰 back up the 🌳 and put them into a small 🪵.

It was making sure its 🥪 was safe in its 🪺.

Soon the busy 🐿 had carried all of the 🌰 into its 🪵.

The 🐿 looked at the 🐻🐑.

It blinked its 👀 and waved its 🐾.

Now the 🐿 was happy. How

wonderful!

Playing is fun, but helping new

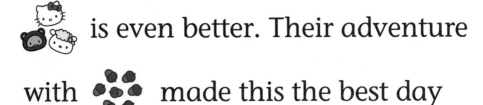 is even better. Their adventure

with 🌰 made this the best day

ever!

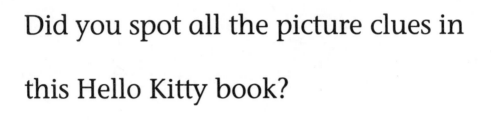

Did you spot all the picture clues in this Hello Kitty book?

Each picture clue is on a flash card. Ask a grown-up to cut out the flash cards. Then try reading the words on the backs of the cards. The pictures will be your clue.

Reading is fun with *Hello Kitty*!

woods	Hello Kitty
sun	Tracy
friends	Fifi

acorns	leaves
home	pinecones
paint	backpack

branch	glue
eyes	tree
tail	squirrel

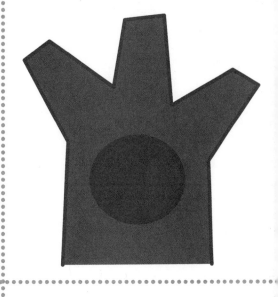

rock	food
hole	bush
nest	log